The Rolling Stones Rock Score

Wise Publications
London/New York/Sydney

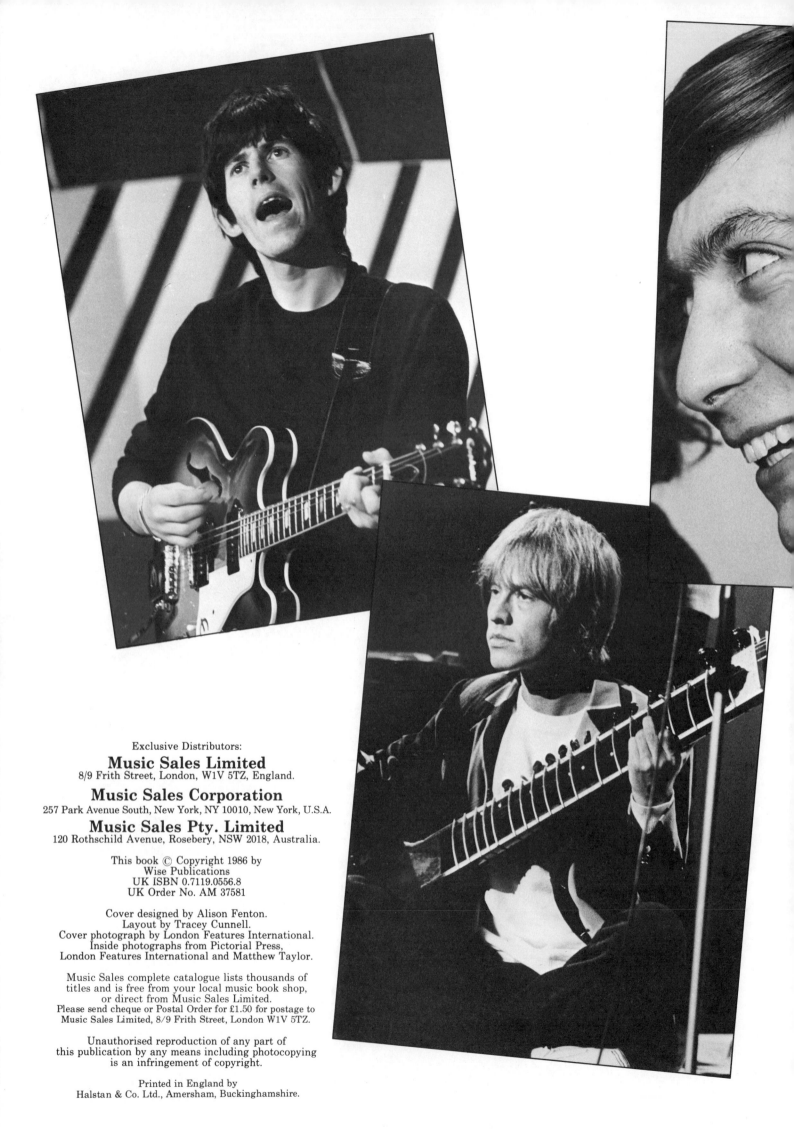

Exclusive Distributors:
Music Sales Limited
8/9 Frith Street, London, W1V 5TZ, England.

Music Sales Corporation
257 Park Avenue South, New York, NY 10010, New York, U.S.A.

Music Sales Pty. Limited
120 Rothschild Avenue, Rosebery, NSW 2018, Australia.

This book © Copyright 1986 by
Wise Publications
UK ISBN 0.7119.0556.8
UK Order No. AM 37581

Cover designed by Alison Fenton.
Layout by Tracey Cunnell.
Cover photograph by London Features International.
Inside photographs from Pictorial Press,
London Features International and Matthew Taylor.

Music Sales complete catalogue lists thousands of
titles and is free from your local music book shop,
or direct from Music Sales Limited.
Please send cheque or Postal Order for £1.50 for postage to
Music Sales Limited, 8/9 Frith Street, London W1V 5TZ.

Printed in England by
Halstan & Co. Ltd., Amersham, Buckinghamshire.

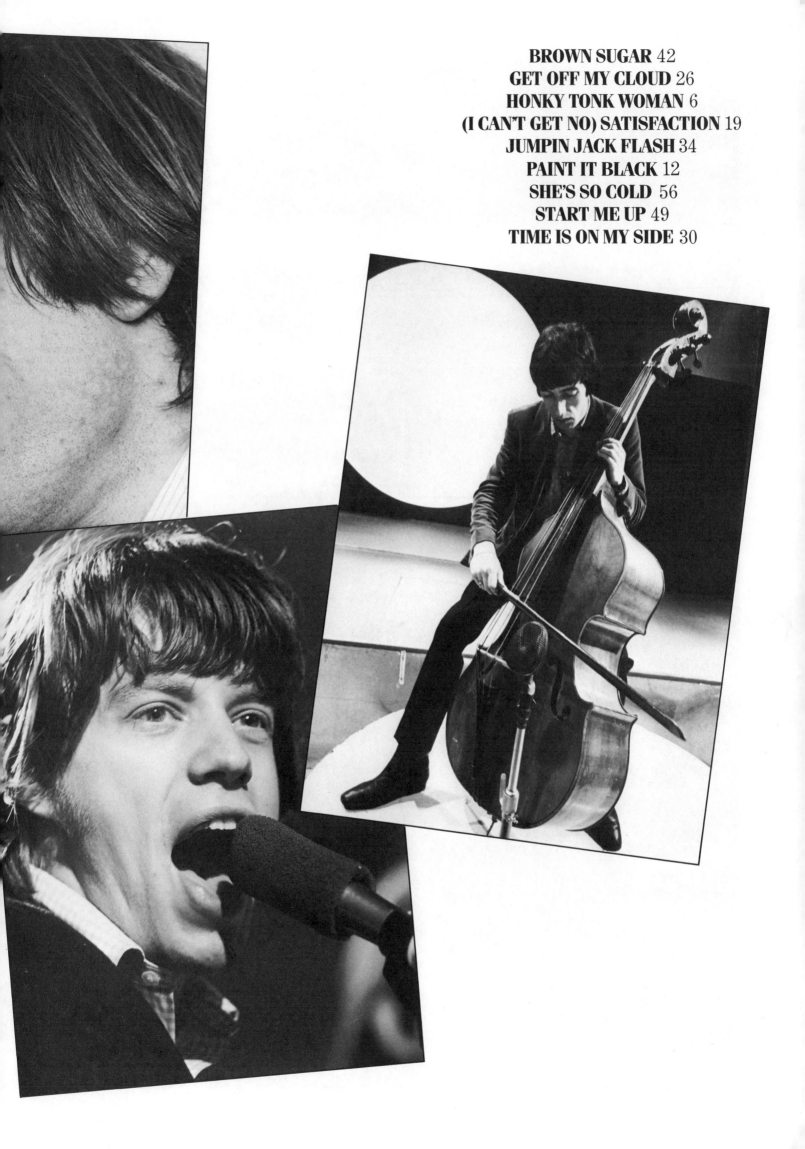

HONKY TONK WOMEN

Words & Music by Mick Jagger & Keith Richard

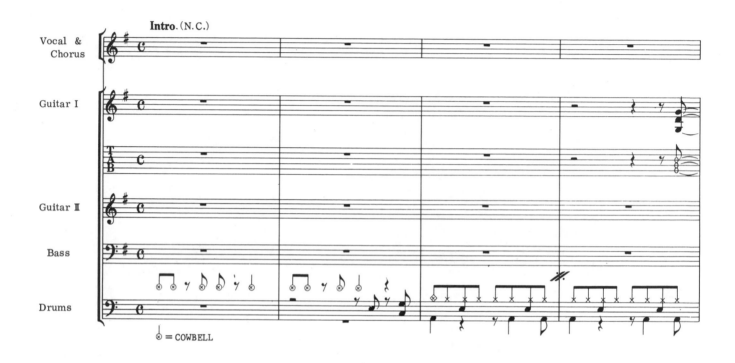

met a gin soaked bar - room Queen in Mem-phis ___   She
played a di - vorc - ee ___ in New ___ York Ci - ty ___   I

tried to take me ___ up stai-rs ___ for a ___ ride   She
had to ___ put ___ up some kind of   a fight ___   The

had to   heave me right ___ a - cross her   should - er ___
la - dy   then she cov - ered me with   Ro - ses ___

7

'Coz I just____ don't seem to drink____ you off____ my mind____
She blew____ my nose and then____ she blew____ my mind____

It's a Hon____

ky tonk____ wo - men____

give me___ give me___ give me___ a Hon-ky Tonk___ Blues

(I)
All right!

9

PAINT IT BLACK

Words & Music by Mick Jagger & Keith Richard

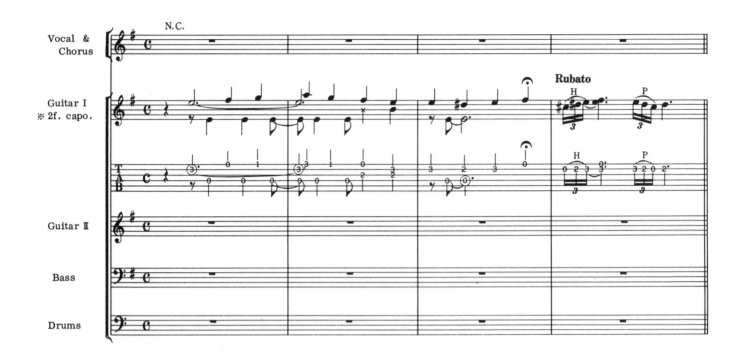

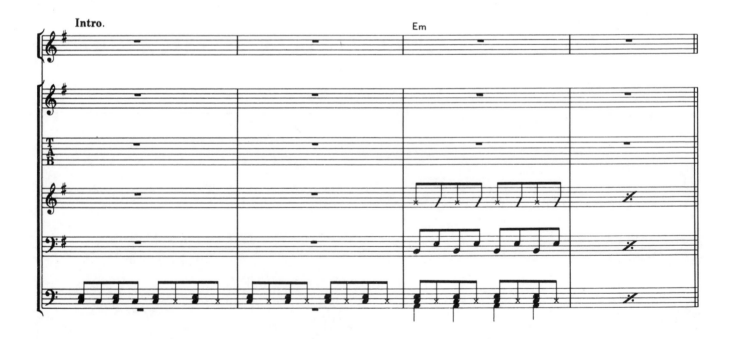

Em D G D A B to ⊕

I have to turn my head un-til__ my dar-kness goes__
Like a new-born baby it just_____ happe-ns e-very day
(It's) not ea-sy fa - cing up__ when your whole world__ is black __

(3 times)

C Em   B
No more will my g-reen sea go turn a dee-per blue__

Em   B
I could not fore-see this thing ha-ppe-ning to you__

14

If I look hard en-ough in - to____ the set - ting sun____

My love will laugh with me____ be - fore_____ the mor - ning comes____

D.S.

Coda

I wan-na see ya

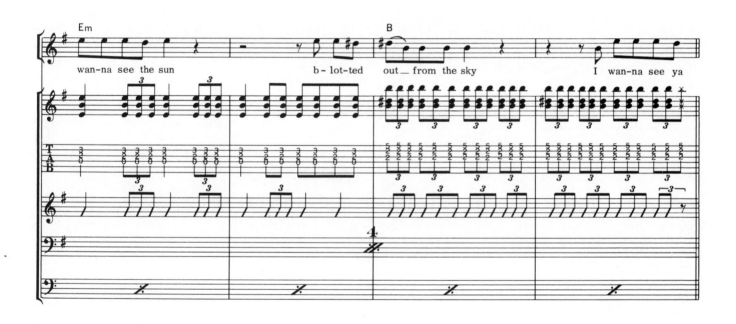

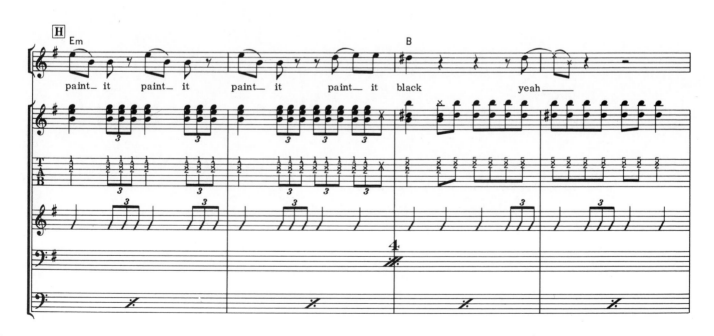

(I CAN'T GET NO) SATISFACTION

Words & Music by Mick Jagger & Keith Richard

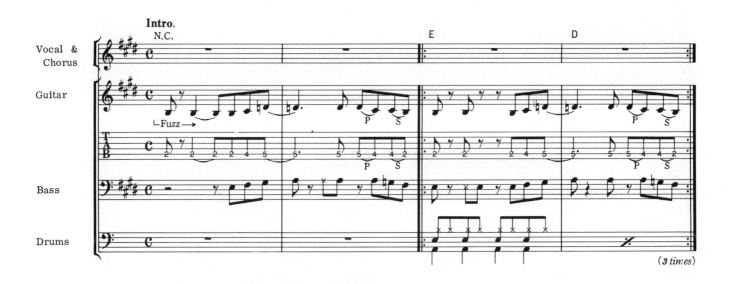

and I've tried _____   and I've tried _____   and I've tried _____

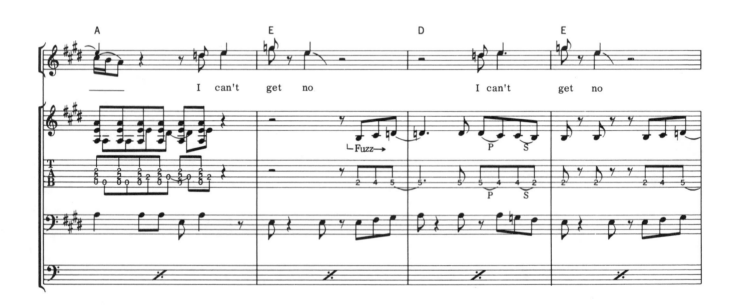

I can't   get   no   I can't   get   no

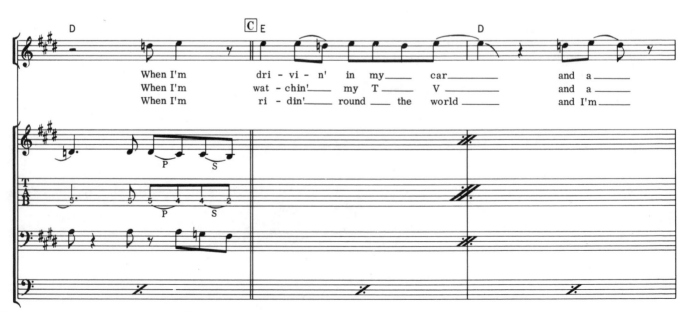

When I'm   dri - vi - n' in my _____ car _____   and a _____
When I'm   wat - chin' _____ my T _____ V _____   and a _____
When I'm   ri - din' _____ round _____ the   world _____   and I'm _____

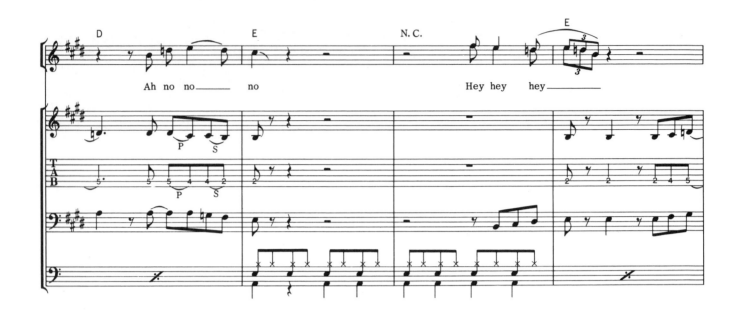

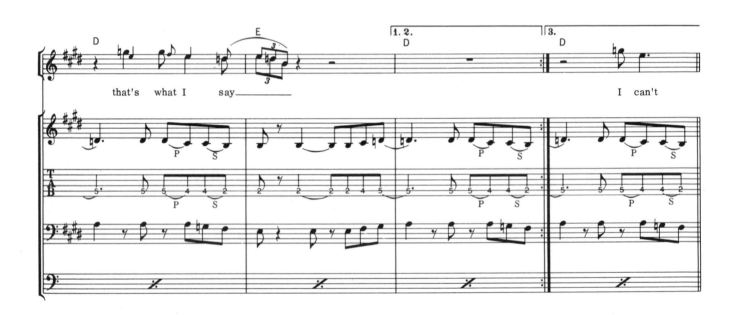

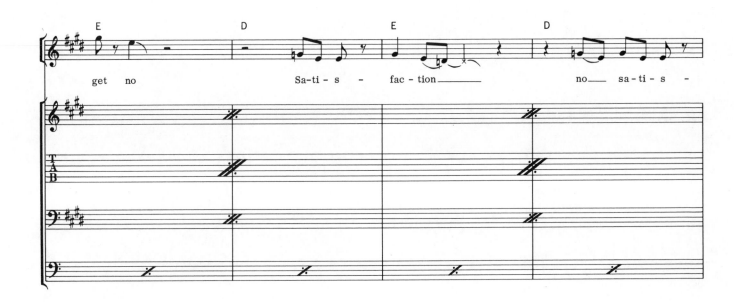

get no ____ Sa-ti - s - fac - tion ____ no ___ sa-ti-s -

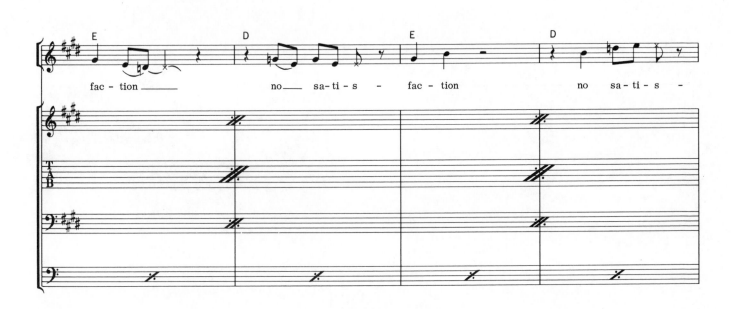

fac - tion ____ no ___ sa-ti-s - fac - tion no sa-ti-s -

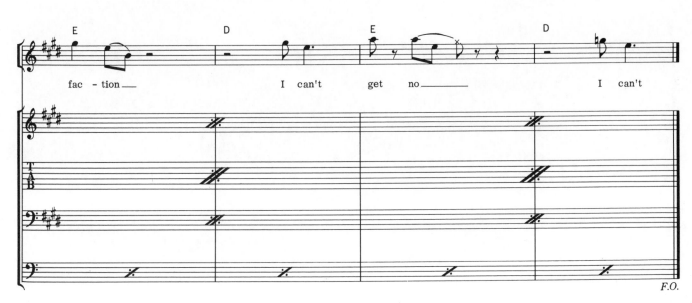

fac - tion ____ I can't get no ____ I can't

F.O.

GET OFF OF MY CLOUD

Words & Music by Mick Jagger & Keith Richard

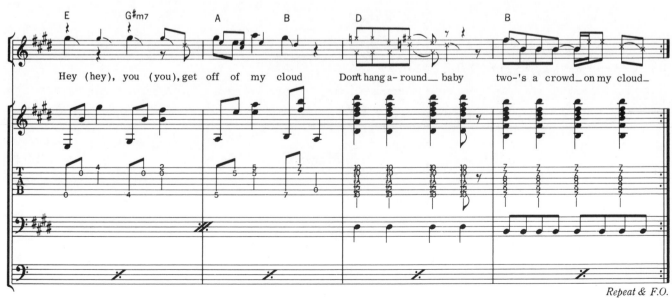

Repeat & F.O.

TIME IS ON MY SIDE

Words & Music by Norman Meade

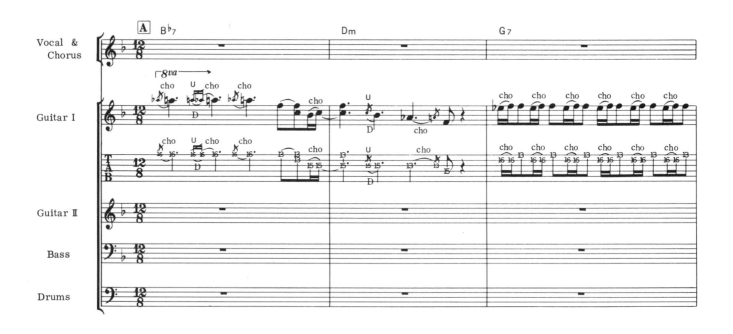

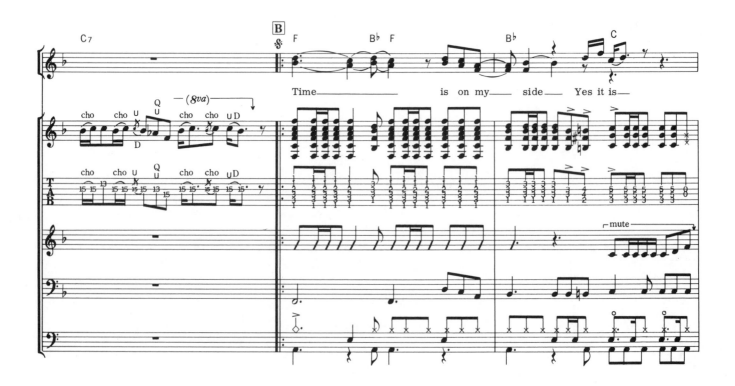

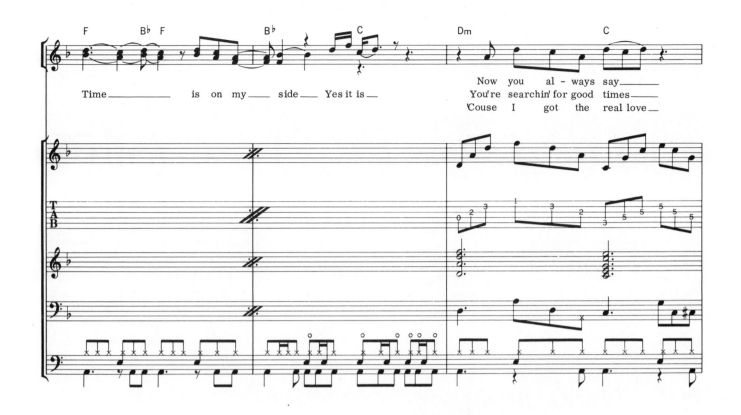

Time _____ is on my ____ side ____ Yes it is ____
Now you al - ways say _____
You're searchin' for good times _____
'Couse I got the real love _____

that you want __ to be free
But just wait and see
the kind that you need

But you'll come __ runnin' back
But bet you would ba - by
I said you were darling
I knew one day

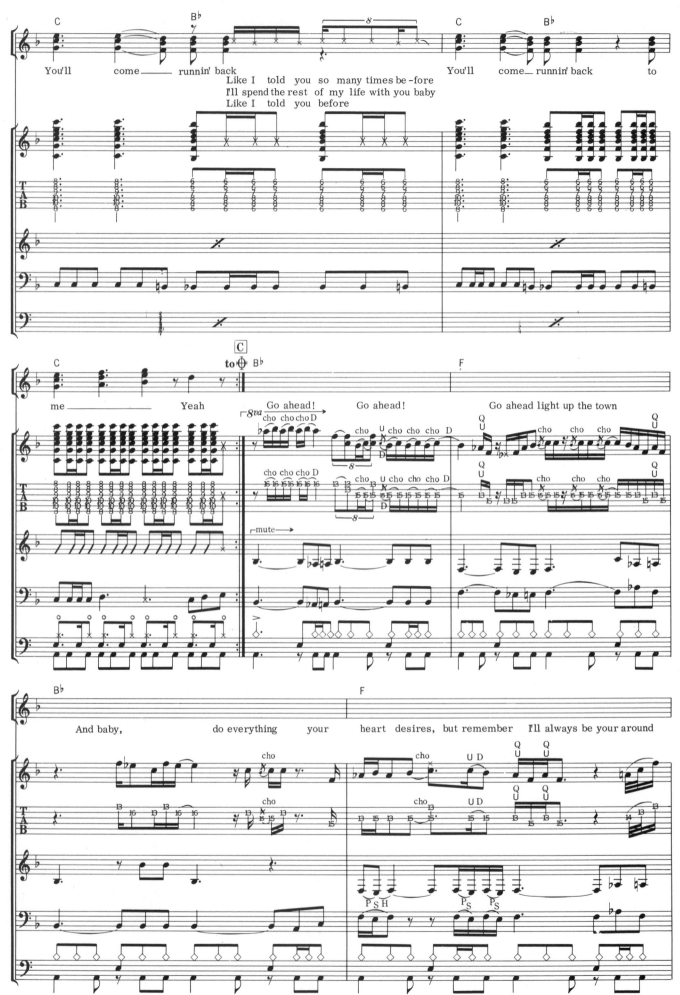

JUMPIN' JACK FLASH

Words & Music by Mick Jagger & Keith Richard

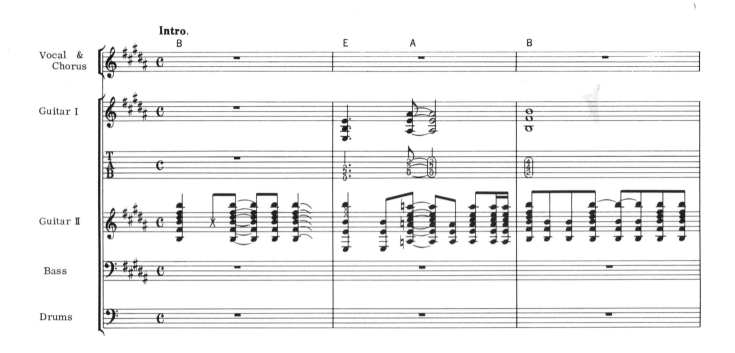

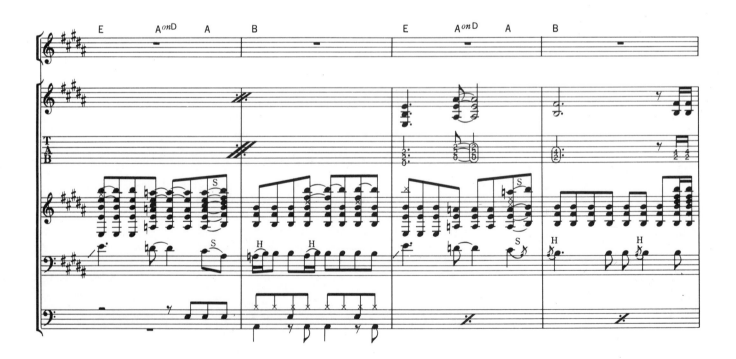

One Two!

I was born _____ in a cross - fire hurri - cane
I was raised _____ by a tooth - less bear - ded hag

And I howled _____ in my ma _____ in the dri - ving rain _____
I was shooled _____ with a strap _____ a - cross _____ my back _____

But it's all _____

right _____ now   In fact it's a gas _____   But it's all _____

right _____   I'm Jum-pin' Jack Flash it's a

36

gas, gas, gas,

gas, gas, gas,

Mh

I was drowned———————— was washed—up and left— for dead
I fell down—————— to my feet— and I saw—they bled————————— Yeah
————, Yeah And I frowned———— at the crumbs— of a crust—of bread———————— Waw
—, yeah, Yeah I was crowned———— with a spike— right— through my head————

(*3 times repeat*)

BROWN SUGAR

Words & Music by Mick Jagger & Keith Richard

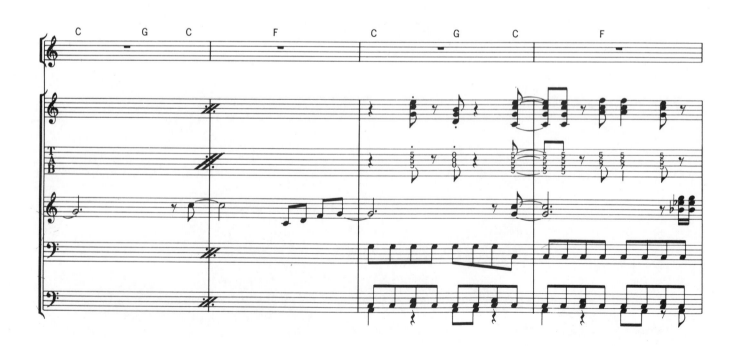

Gold

A

— coast slave ship bound for cot - ton fields sold ___ in a mar - ket down in

— beat cold ___ Eng - lish blood run hot ___ La - dy of the house wond' - rin

just like a young girl Should __ A ha ha __ Wow!

just like a young girl Should __ A ha ha __ Hey !

just like a young girl Should __ A ha ha __ Now

Wow !

Drum ～ Sax Solo ～

(3 times)

Aah

I bet your ma-ma was a Tent show queen and

all her girl-friends were sweet six-teen I'm no school boy but I know what I like You

should have heard him just a-round mid-night Brown Su-gar how

46

How come you   how come you tasyers so   good——   Yeah—— - yeah—— yeah—— wow!
Just like a   just like a   young girl should——   Yeah—

START ME UP
Words & Music by Mick Jagger & Keith Richard

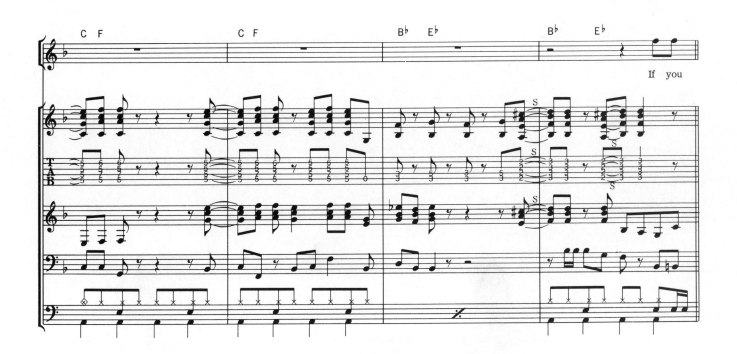

start me up   you can start me up I   nev-er stop   nev-er stop   nev-er stop   nev-er stop

You make a   grown man   cry⎯⎯⎯⎯   You make a   grown man   cry⎯⎯
Don't make a   grown man   cry⎯⎯⎯⎯   Don't make a   grown man   cry⎯⎯
You make a   grown man   cry⎯⎯⎯⎯   You make a   grown man   cry⎯⎯

You make a   grown man   cry⎯⎯⎯⎯   Spread out the oil   the ga-so-line
Don't make a   grown man   cry⎯⎯⎯⎯   My eyes di-late   my lips go green
You make a   grown man   cry⎯⎯⎯⎯   Ride like the wind   at dou-ble speed

start it up___   nev-er nev-er nev-er   Yeah___

D.S.

Start it up   love the day when we will   nev-er stop   nev-er stop   nev-er nev-er nev-er stop

tough me up   nev-er stop   nev-er stop

54

SHE'S SO COLD

Words & Music by Mick Jagger & Keith Richard

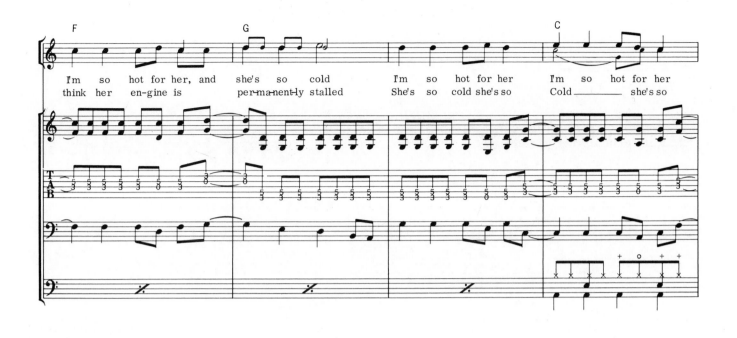

I'm so hot for her, and she's so cold
When I touched her my hand just froze

Yes, I've   Yeah   I'm so hot for her
She's so cold she's so

I'm so hot for her   I'm so hot for her   she's so cold___ Put your
cold___   I think she was born in an arc - tic zone

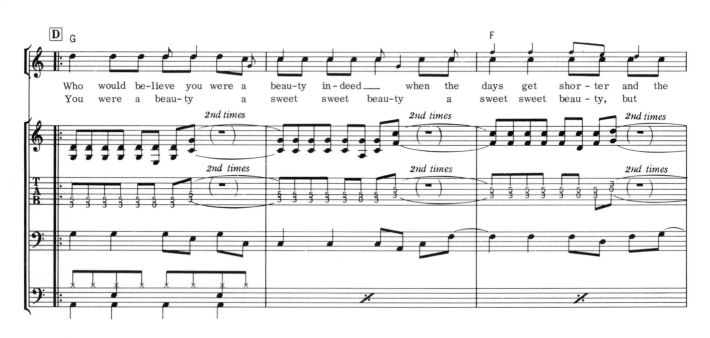

Who would be-lieve you were a beau-ty in-deed___ when the days get shor-ter and the
You were a beau-ty a sweet sweet beau-ty a sweet sweet beau-ty, but

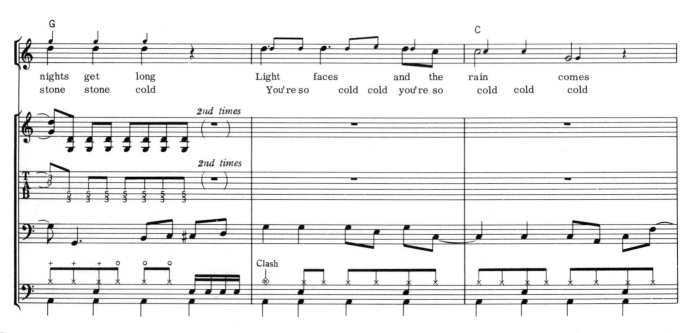

nights get long Light faces and the rain comes
stone stone cold You're so cold cold you're so cold cold cold

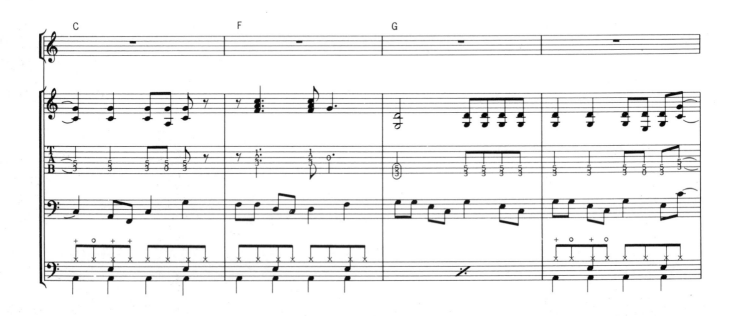

F.O.

2/97 (27199)

The
Rock
Scores

Note for note.

Word for word.

Just like the famous recordings.

Now you can play all the greatest rock music.

The Rock Scores.

Authentic off-the-record transcriptions.
Every note for every instrument
plus lyrics and all the vocal lines.

THE COLLECTIONS

Rock'n'Roll

Great Balls Of Fire
That'll Be The Day
Summertime Blues
Rock Around The Clock
At The Hop
Tutti Frutti
Good Golly Miss Molly
Be-Bop-A-Lula

AM77108

Pop Score

Every Breath You Take
(The Police)
Let's Dance *(Chris Rea)*
No Woman, No Cry
*(Bob Marley & The
Wailers)*
The Lady In Red
(Chris de Burgh)
Walk Of Life *(Dire Straits)*
Wonderful Tonight
(Eric Clapton)

AM84211

Heavy Metal

Sweet Child O'Mine
(Guns n'Roses)
Out Of Sight, Out Of Mind
(Anthrax)
Born To Be My Baby
(Bon Jovi)
Heatseeker *(AC/DC)*
Can I Play With Madness?
(Iron Maiden)

AM 76522

60's & 70's

All Right Now *(Free)*
A Whiter Shade Of Pale
(Procol Harum)
Bus Stop *(The Hollies)*
Get It On *(T. Rex)*
Let's Spend The Night
Together *(The Rolling
Stones)*
My Generation *(The Who)*
Paranoid *(Black Sabbath)*
Smoke On The Water
(Deep Purple)
While My Guitar Gently
Weeps *(The Beatles)*

AM 72620

70's

Aqualung *(Jethro Tull)*
Layla *(Derek And
The Dominoes)*
Rock'n'Roll Damnation
(AC/DC)
Smoke On The Water
(Deep Purple)
Sultans Of Swing
(Dire Straits)

AM 79567

80's

Addicted To Love
(Robert Palmer)
Don't You *(Forget
About Me) (Simple Minds)*
It's Only Love *(Bryan
Adams)*
Money For Nothing
(Dire Straits)
Private Dancer
(Tina Turner)
Rebel Yell *(Billy Idol)*

AM81720

THE ARTISTS

AC/DC

Back In Black
Flick Of The Switch
For Those About To Rock
Hell's Bells
Highway To Hell
Rock'n'Roll Damnation
Touch Too Much

AM63330

Beatles 1

All My Loving
Day Tripper
A Hard Day's Night
I Feel Fine
If I Fell
I Want To Hold Your Hand
Let It Be
Paperback Writer
Please, Please Me
She Loves You
Something
Yesterday

NO18442

Beatles 2

Can't Buy Me Love
Get Back
Good Day Sunshine
Got To Get You Into My
Life
Ticket To Ride
We Can Work It Out

NO 90413

Ritchie Blackmore

Mean Streak
Vielleicht Das Nächster
Zeit (Maybe Next Time)
All Night Long
Knocking At Your Back
Door
A Gypsy's Kiss
Can't Happen Here
Long Live Rock'n'Roll
Since You've Been Gone

AM67067

Bon Jovi

Let It Rock
You Give Love A Bad
Name
Livin' On A Prayer
Social Disease
Wanted Dead Or Alive
I'd Die For You
Never Say Goodbye
Raise Your Hands

AM69642

Eric Clapton 1

Bad Love
I Can't Stand It
Lay Down Sally
Layla
Miss You

AM83551

Eric Clapton 2

After Midnight
Badge
Forever Man
Tell The Truth
The Shape You're In
Too Bad

AM83577

Phil Collins

Don't You Lose My
Number
Easy Lover
Inside Out
One More Night
Sussudio

AM66556

Cream

Crossroads
I Feel Free
Strange Brew
Sunshine Of Your Love
Tales Of Brave Ulysses
White Room

AM 83585

The Doors

Hello, I Love You
Light My Fire
Love Me Two Times
Riders On The Storm
You're Lost, Little Girl

AM73917

Bob Dylan

I'll Be Your Baby Tonight
If Not For You
Just Like A Woman
Knockin' On Heaven's
Door
Lay, Lady, Lay
Quinn The Eskimo
(The Mighty Quinn)

AM79021

Genesis

Abacab
Afterglow
Follow You, Follow Me
Mama
That's All
Turn It On Again

AM66564

INXS

Burn For You
Dancing On The Jetty
Original Sin
The One Thing
The Swing

AM82157

The Rock Scores.

Presented in guitar tablature *and* standard notation.

Iron Maiden

Innocent Exile
Killers
Phantom Of The Opera
Remember Tomorrow
Running Free

AM37573

Jethro Tull

A New Day Yesterday
Aqualung
Cross Eyed Mary
Living In The Past
Locomotive Breath

AM79013

Billy Joel

A Matter Of Trust
Honesty
Just The Way You Are
My Life
Pressure
The Stranger
Uptown Girl
You May Be Right

AM70210

Elton John

Crocodile Rock
Don't Go Breaking My
Heart
I Guess That's Why They
Call It The Blues
I'm Still Standing
Saturday Night's All Right
For Fighting
The Bitch Is Back

AM84567

Huey Lewis And The News

Doin' It (All For My Baby)
Do You Believe In Love?
Hope You Love Me Like
You Say You Do
If This Is It
I Want A New Drug
Stuck With You
The Power Of Love
Whole Lotta Lovin'

AM71085

Rolling Stones 1

Brown Sugar
Get Off Of My Cloud
Honky Tonk Women
Jumpin' Jack Flash
Paint It Black
Satisfaction
She's So Cold
Start Me Up
Time Is On My Side

AM 37581

Rolling Stones 2

Gimme Shelter
19th Nervous Breakdown
Street Fighting Man
Sympathy For the Devil
(This Could Be) The Last
Time
Tumbling Dice

AM89230

Bruce Springsteen

Born In The USA
Cover Me
Dancing In The Dark
Downbound Train
Glory Days
I'm On Fire
My Hometown
No Surrender

AM 63348

Sting

Consider Me Gone
Englishman In New York
Fragile
If You Love Somebody Set
Them Free
Straight To My Heart
The Secret Marriage
They Dance Alone (Gueca
Solo)

AM 76266

U2

I Still Haven't Found What
I'm Looking For
Pride (In The Name Of
Love)
Sunday Bloody Sunday
The Unforgettable Fire
Where The Streets Have
No Name

AM 72562

The Who

I Can See For Miles
My Generation
Pinball Wizard
Substitute
The Kids Are Alright

AM77793

Vocal

E.Guitar 1

Bass

Drums